Let's Share

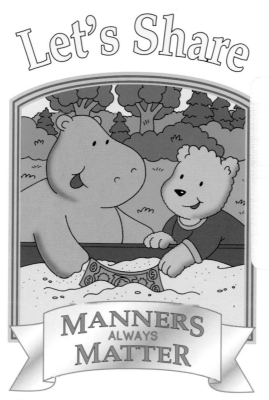

MANNERS ALWAYS MATTER

Illustrated by Lance Raichert
Written by Jason Blundy

Bear and Hippo were playing together when they saw something buried in the sandbox. They reached in together to pull the object out.

"My goodness," said Bear, "it's a dollar."

"What should we do with it?" asked Hippo.

"We should see if it belongs to someone," Bear said wisely.

The two of them walked around the playground until they happened upon Skunk.

"Hey, Skunk. We found a dollar," said Bear, "and we're trying to find its owner."

"I wish it were mine. I could use it to buy a new book," said Skunk.

Bear and Hippo said goodbye and left to see if anyone else had lost a dollar.

They saw Mouse and Piggy playing in the sandbox and checked to see if it belonged to either of them.

"I wish I had a dollar to lose," said Mouse.

"Me too," Piggy said, laughing. "You guys should buy some candy with it. That's what I would do."

"That would be nice," said Bear, "but somebody might need this dollar."

The two friends kept searching. They saw Kitty and Bunny and went to see if either one had lost the money, but neither had.

"Maybe you could put up a sign so the owner will know where to find you," said Kitty.

"Yeah," Bunny said, "that way you're sure to find the owner, if there is one."

Hippo thought the sign was a good idea, so he and Bear posted one on the fence surrounding the playground.

"We'll find the owner of this dollar for sure now," said Hippo confidently.

"Let's set up a table and wait for the owner to stop by. If no one claims it by the end of the day, then we can keep it for ourselves," Bear said.

They waited all day, but nobody came to claim the dollar. Their friends stopped by from time to time and offered advice on how to spend the money. Finally, the sun began to set. Bear and Hippo decided to call it a night.

"Okay. We'll bury the dollar until tomorrow and then we can safely say it is ours," said Bear.

The next morning they met to dig up the dollar, but it was gone. Just then Turtle walked up with a dollar in his hand.

"Look what I found buried over there," he said.

"That's mine!" Hippo and Bear yelled together.

Suddenly Bear realized how silly they were being.

"I know," he said. "Let's share."

Let's Share

Bear and Hippo wanted to do the right thing, but then they got greedy. It wasn't until they shared that everyone was happy. Friends always have more fun when they share.